MAMA BEAR Kusi's
weekly
MEAL PLANNER

A 52-WEEK MENU PLANNER

WITH GROCERY LIST FOR PLANNING YOUR MEALS

ASHLEY KUSI

Mama Bear Kusi's Weekly Meal Planner: A 52-Week Menu Planner with Grocery List for Planning Your Meals.

Created by Ashley and Marcus Kusi.

ISBN-13: 978-0-9987291-4-5

ISBN-10: 0-9987291-4-0

THIS MEAL PLANNER
BELONGS TO:

_____

GETTING STARTED

Thank you so much for choosing to use my weekly meal planner! This planner was created with the intention to fit the needs of different meal planning styles. Whether you track and plan weekly, bi-weekly, or monthly, this meal planner will meet your needs.

Each week, you will find a new menu to plan as well as a page to keep track of your budget, a notes section to journal, log information or track progress, a shopping list page, and a monthly freezer inventory page to make sure nothing goes to waste.

In the back pages, I have included:

- » Special Event Meal Plan pages to stay organized for your next dinner party, or holiday social.

- » Conversion Chart for Baking.

- » Conversion Chart for Liquid.

- » How to Alter a Recipe page if you want to *double a recipe*, or even *cut the recipe in half.*

- » Baking Substitutions page.

- » Staples page of what I typically keep in my kitchen as well as a page to write your own staples.

- » Favorite Meals page for you to write down your crowd-pleasing dishes to jumpstart planning your weekly food menu.

- » Recipe pages for you to copy or create your own sweet or savory dishes!

I hope this weekly meal planner helps you simplify, stay organized, and sets you up for success in all your meal planning needs. If it does, feel free to leave me an honest review on Amazon.

Lastly, visit www.mamabearkusi.com/fruittartrecipe to add my Mini Fruit Tart recipe that is grain-free, dairy-free, autoimmune paleo friendly, and vegan to your first weekly menu!

Thank you again,
Mama Bear Kusi AKA Ashley Kusi

MONTH OF: _____ WEEK OF: _____

DINNERS

_____
_____
_____
_____
_____
_____

BREAKFASTS

_____
_____
_____
_____
_____
_____

LUNCHES

_____
_____
_____
_____
_____

SNACKS

_____
_____
_____
_____
_____

SHOPPING LIST

PRICE	ITEM	STORE	NOTES

BUDGET FOR THE WEEK: _____

STORE	AMOUNT	BALANCE
_____	_____	_____
_____	_____	_____
_____	_____	_____
_____	_____	_____

NOTES

_____

_____

_____

_____

_____

_____

_____

_____

_____

_____

_____

_____

FREEZER INVENTORY

DATE ENTERED	ITEM	QTY	DATE EXPIRES	# USED

MONTH OF: _____   WEEK OF: _____

DINNERS	BREAKFASTS
_____	_____
_____	_____
_____	_____
_____	_____
_____	_____
_____	_____
_____	_____

LUNCHES	SNACKS
_____	_____
_____	_____
_____	_____
_____	_____
_____	_____
_____	_____

SHOPPING LIST

PRICE	ITEM	STORE	NOTES

BUDGET FOR THE WEEK: _____

STORE	AMOUNT	BALANCE
_____	_____	_____
_____	_____	_____
_____	_____	_____
_____	_____	_____

NOTES

_____

_____

_____

_____

_____

_____

_____

_____

_____

_____

_____

_____

MONTH OF: _____   WEEK OF: _____

DINNERS	BREAKFASTS
_____	_____
_____	_____
_____	_____
_____	_____
_____	_____
_____	_____
_____	_____

LUNCHES	SNACKS
_____	_____
_____	_____
_____	_____
_____	_____
_____	_____
_____	_____

SHOPPING LIST

PRICE	ITEM	STORE	NOTES

BUDGET FOR THE WEEK: _____

STORE	AMOUNT	BALANCE
_____	_____	_____
_____	_____	_____
_____	_____	_____
_____	_____	_____

NOTES

_____

_____

_____

_____

_____

_____

_____

_____

_____

_____

_____

_____

MONTH OF: _____   WEEK OF: _____

DINNERS	BREAKFASTS
_____	_____
_____	_____
_____	_____
_____	_____
_____	_____
_____	_____
_____	_____

LUNCHES	SNACKS
_____	_____
_____	_____
_____	_____
_____	_____
_____	_____
_____	_____

SHOPPING LIST

PRICE	ITEM	STORE	NOTES

BUDGET FOR THE WEEK: _____

STORE	AMOUNT	BALANCE
_____	_____	_____
_____	_____	_____
_____	_____	_____
_____	_____	_____

NOTES

_____

_____

_____

_____

_____

_____

_____

_____

_____

_____

_____

_____

_____

MONTH OF: _____   WEEK OF: _____

DINNERS

_____

_____

_____

_____

_____

_____

BREAKFASTS

_____

_____

_____

_____

_____

_____

LUNCHES

_____

_____

_____

_____

_____

SNACKS

_____

_____

_____

_____

_____

SHOPPING LIST

PRICE	ITEM	STORE	NOTES

BUDGET FOR THE WEEK: _____

STORE	AMOUNT	BALANCE
_____	_____	_____
_____	_____	_____
_____	_____	_____
_____	_____	_____

NOTES

_____

_____

_____

_____

_____

_____

_____

_____

_____

_____

_____

_____

_____

FREEZER INVENTORY

DATE ENTERED	ITEM	QTY	DATE EXPIRES	# USED

MONTH OF: _____ WEEK OF: _____

DINNERS

_____

_____

_____

_____

_____

_____

BREAKFASTS

_____

_____

_____

_____

_____

_____

LUNCHES

_____

_____

_____

_____

_____

_____

SNACKS

_____

_____

_____

_____

_____

_____

SHOPPING LIST

PRICE	ITEM	STORE	NOTES

BUDGET FOR THE WEEK: _____

STORE	AMOUNT	BALANCE
_____	_____	_____
_____	_____	_____
_____	_____	_____
_____	_____	_____

NOTES

_____

_____

_____

_____

_____

_____

_____

_____

_____

_____

_____

_____

MONTH OF: _____   WEEK OF: _____

DINNERS

_____

_____

_____

_____

_____

_____

_____

BREAKFASTS

_____

_____

_____

_____

_____

_____

_____

LUNCHES

_____

_____

_____

_____

_____

_____

SNACKS

_____

_____

_____

_____

_____

_____

SHOPPING LIST

PRICE	ITEM	STORE	NOTES

BUDGET FOR THE WEEK: _____

STORE	AMOUNT	BALANCE
_____	_____	_____
_____	_____	_____
_____	_____	_____
_____	_____	_____

NOTES

_____

_____

_____

_____

_____

_____

_____

_____

_____

_____

_____

_____

_____

MONTH OF: _____   WEEK OF: _____

DINNERS	BREAKFASTS
_____	_____
_____	_____
_____	_____
_____	_____
_____	_____
_____	_____

LUNCHES	SNACKS
_____	_____
_____	_____
_____	_____
_____	_____
_____	_____

SHOPPING LIST

PRICE	ITEM	STORE	NOTES

BUDGET FOR THE WEEK: _____

STORE	AMOUNT	BALANCE
_____	_____	_____
_____	_____	_____
_____	_____	_____
_____	_____	_____

NOTES

_____

_____

_____

_____

_____

_____

_____

_____

_____

_____

_____

_____

MONTH OF: _____   WEEK OF: _____

DINNERS

_____

_____

_____

_____

_____

_____

BREAKFASTS

_____

_____

_____

_____

_____

_____

LUNCHES

_____

_____

_____

_____

_____

SNACKS

_____

_____

_____

_____

_____

SHOPPING LIST

PRICE	ITEM	STORE	NOTES

BUDGET FOR THE WEEK: _____

STORE	AMOUNT	BALANCE
_____	_____	_____
_____	_____	_____
_____	_____	_____
_____	_____	_____

NOTES

_____

_____

_____

_____

_____

_____

_____

_____

_____

_____

_____

FREEZER INVENTORY

DATE ENTERED	ITEM	QTY	DATE EXPIRES	# USED
_____	_____	____	_____	____
_____	_____	____	_____	____
_____	_____	____	_____	____
_____	_____	____	_____	____
_____	_____	____	_____	____
_____	_____	____	_____	____
_____	_____	____	_____	____
_____	_____	____	_____	____
_____	_____	____	_____	____
_____	_____	____	_____	____
_____	_____	____	_____	____
_____	_____	____	_____	____
_____	_____	____	_____	____
_____	_____	____	_____	____
_____	_____	____	_____	____
_____	_____	____	_____	____
_____	_____	____	_____	____
_____	_____	____	_____	____

MONTH OF: _____ WEEK OF: _____

DINNERS

_____

_____

_____

_____

_____

_____

_____

BREAKFASTS

_____

_____

_____

_____

_____

_____

_____

LUNCHES

_____

_____

_____

_____

_____

_____

SNACKS

_____

_____

_____

_____

_____

_____

SHOPPING LIST

PRICE	ITEM	STORE	NOTES

BUDGET FOR THE WEEK: _____

STORE	AMOUNT	BALANCE
_____	_____	_____
_____	_____	_____
_____	_____	_____
_____	_____	_____

NOTES

_____

_____

_____

_____

_____

_____

_____

_____

_____

_____

_____

MONTH OF: _____   WEEK OF: _____

DINNERS	BREAKFASTS
_____	_____
_____	_____
_____	_____
_____	_____
_____	_____
_____	_____

LUNCHES	SNACKS
_____	_____
_____	_____
_____	_____
_____	_____
_____	_____

SHOPPING LIST

PRICE	ITEM	STORE	NOTES

BUDGET FOR THE WEEK: _____

STORE	AMOUNT	BALANCE
_____	_____	_____
_____	_____	_____
_____	_____	_____
_____	_____	_____

NOTES

_____

_____

_____

_____

_____

_____

_____

_____

_____

_____

_____

_____

MONTH OF: _____ WEEK OF: _____

DINNERS	BREAKFASTS
_____	_____
_____	_____
_____	_____
_____	_____
_____	_____
_____	_____

LUNCHES	SNACKS
_____	_____
_____	_____
_____	_____
_____	_____
_____	_____

SHOPPING LIST

PRICE	ITEM	STORE	NOTES

BUDGET FOR THE WEEK: _____

STORE	AMOUNT	BALANCE
_____	_____	_____
_____	_____	_____
_____	_____	_____
_____	_____	_____

NOTES

_____

_____

_____

_____

_____

_____

_____

_____

_____

_____

_____

_____

MONTH OF: _____   WEEK OF: _____

DINNERS	BREAKFASTS
_____	_____
_____	_____
_____	_____
_____	_____
_____	_____
_____	_____
_____	_____

LUNCHES	SNACKS
_____	_____
_____	_____
_____	_____
_____	_____
_____	_____
_____	_____

SHOPPING LIST

PRICE	ITEM	STORE	NOTES

BUDGET FOR THE WEEK: _____

STORE	AMOUNT	BALANCE
_____	_____	_____
_____	_____	_____
_____	_____	_____
_____	_____	_____

NOTES

_____

_____

_____

_____

_____

_____

_____

_____

_____

_____

_____

_____

FREEZER INVENTORY

DATE ENTERED	ITEM	QTY	DATE EXPIRES	# USED

MONTH OF: _____   WEEK OF: _____

DINNERS

_____

_____

_____

_____

_____

_____

BREAKFASTS

_____

_____

_____

_____

_____

_____

LUNCHES

_____

_____

_____

_____

_____

_____

SNACKS

_____

_____

_____

_____

_____

_____

SHOPPING LIST

PRICE	ITEM	STORE	NOTES

BUDGET FOR THE WEEK: _____

STORE	AMOUNT	BALANCE
_____	_____	_____
_____	_____	_____
_____	_____	_____
_____	_____	_____

NOTES

_____

_____

_____

_____

_____

_____

_____

_____

_____

_____

_____

_____

_____

MONTH OF: _____ WEEK OF: _____

DINNERS	BREAKFASTS
_____	_____
_____	_____
_____	_____
_____	_____
_____	_____
_____	_____

LUNCHES	SNACKS
_____	_____
_____	_____
_____	_____
_____	_____
_____	_____

SHOPPING LIST

PRICE	ITEM	STORE	NOTES

BUDGET FOR THE WEEK: _____

STORE	AMOUNT	BALANCE
_____	_____	_____
_____	_____	_____
_____	_____	_____
_____	_____	_____

NOTES

_____

_____

_____

_____

_____

_____

_____

_____

_____

_____

_____

_____

MONTH OF: _____   WEEK OF: _____

DINNERS
_____
_____
_____
_____
_____
_____
_____

BREAKFASTS
_____
_____
_____
_____
_____
_____
_____

LUNCHES
_____
_____
_____
_____
_____
_____

SNACKS
_____
_____
_____
_____
_____
_____

SHOPPING LIST

PRICE	ITEM	STORE	NOTES

BUDGET FOR THE WEEK: _____

STORE	AMOUNT	BALANCE
_____	_____	_____
_____	_____	_____
_____	_____	_____
_____	_____	_____

NOTES

_____

_____

_____

_____

_____

_____

_____

_____

_____

_____

_____

_____

MONTH OF: _____ WEEK OF: _____

DINNERS	BREAKFASTS

_____   _____

_____   _____

_____   _____

_____   _____

_____   _____

_____   _____

LUNCHES	SNACKS

_____   _____

_____   _____

_____   _____

_____   _____

SHOPPING LIST

PRICE	ITEM	STORE	NOTES

BUDGET FOR THE WEEK: _____

STORE	AMOUNT	BALANCE
_____	_____	_____
_____	_____	_____
_____	_____	_____
_____	_____	_____

NOTES

_____

_____

_____

_____

_____

_____

_____

_____

_____

_____

_____

_____

FREEZER INVENTORY

DATE ENTERED	ITEM	QTY	DATE EXPIRES	# USED

MONTH OF: _____   WEEK OF: _____

DINNERS

_____

_____

_____

_____

_____

_____

BREAKFASTS

_____

_____

_____

_____

_____

_____

LUNCHES

_____

_____

_____

_____

_____

SNACKS

_____

_____

_____

_____

_____

SHOPPING LIST

PRICE	ITEM	STORE	NOTES

BUDGET FOR THE WEEK: _____

STORE	AMOUNT	BALANCE
_____	_____	_____
_____	_____	_____
_____	_____	_____
_____	_____	_____

NOTES

_____

_____

_____

_____

_____

_____

_____

_____

_____

_____

_____

_____

MONTH OF: _____ WEEK OF: _____

DINNERS

_____

_____

_____

_____

_____

_____

_____

BREAKFASTS

_____

_____

_____

_____

_____

_____

_____

LUNCHES

_____

_____

_____

_____

_____

_____

SNACKS

_____

_____

_____

_____

_____

_____

SHOPPING LIST

PRICE	ITEM	STORE	NOTES

BUDGET FOR THE WEEK: _____

STORE	AMOUNT	BALANCE
_____	_____	_____
_____	_____	_____
_____	_____	_____
_____	_____	_____

NOTES

_____

_____

_____

_____

_____

_____

_____

_____

_____

_____

_____

_____

MONTH OF: _____   WEEK OF: _____

DINNERS	BREAKFASTS
_____	_____
_____	_____
_____	_____
_____	_____
_____	_____
_____	_____
_____	_____

LUNCHES	SNACKS
_____	_____
_____	_____
_____	_____
_____	_____
_____	_____

SHOPPING LIST

PRICE	ITEM	STORE	NOTES

BUDGET FOR THE WEEK: _____

STORE	AMOUNT	BALANCE
_____	_____	_____
_____	_____	_____
_____	_____	_____
_____	_____	_____

NOTES

_____

_____

_____

_____

_____

_____

_____

_____

_____

_____

_____

_____

MONTH OF: _____   WEEK OF: _____

DINNERS	BREAKFASTS
_____	_____
_____	_____
_____	_____
_____	_____
_____	_____
_____	_____
_____	_____

LUNCHES	SNACKS
_____	_____
_____	_____
_____	_____
_____	_____
_____	_____
_____	_____
_____	_____

SHOPPING LIST

PRICE	ITEM	STORE	NOTES

BUDGET FOR THE WEEK: _____

STORE	AMOUNT	BALANCE
_____	_____	_____
_____	_____	_____
_____	_____	_____
_____	_____	_____

NOTES

_____

_____

_____

_____

_____

_____

_____

_____

_____

_____

_____

_____

_____

FREEZER INVENTORY

DATE ENTERED	ITEM	QTY	DATE EXPIRES	# USED
_____	_____	_____	_____	_____
_____	_____	_____	_____	_____
_____	_____	_____	_____	_____
_____	_____	_____	_____	_____
_____	_____	_____	_____	_____
_____	_____	_____	_____	_____
_____	_____	_____	_____	_____
_____	_____	_____	_____	_____
_____	_____	_____	_____	_____
_____	_____	_____	_____	_____
_____	_____	_____	_____	_____
_____	_____	_____	_____	_____
_____	_____	_____	_____	_____
_____	_____	_____	_____	_____
_____	_____	_____	_____	_____
_____	_____	_____	_____	_____
_____	_____	_____	_____	_____
_____	_____	_____	_____	_____

MONTH OF: _____ WEEK OF: _____

DINNERS

_____

_____

_____

_____

_____

_____

_____

BREAKFASTS

_____

_____

_____

_____

_____

_____

_____

LUNCHES

_____

_____

_____

_____

_____

_____

_____

SNACKS

_____

_____

_____

_____

_____

_____

_____

SHOPPING LIST

PRICE	ITEM	STORE	NOTES

BUDGET FOR THE WEEK: _____

STORE	AMOUNT	BALANCE
_____	_____	_____
_____	_____	_____
_____	_____	_____
_____	_____	_____

NOTES

_____

_____

_____

_____

_____

_____

_____

_____

_____

_____

_____

_____

MONTH OF: _____   WEEK OF: _____

DINNERS	BREAKFASTS
_____	_____
_____	_____
_____	_____
_____	_____
_____	_____
_____	_____
_____	_____

LUNCHES	SNACKS
_____	_____
_____	_____
_____	_____
_____	_____
_____	_____

SHOPPING LIST

PRICE	ITEM	STORE	NOTES

BUDGET FOR THE WEEK: _____

STORE	AMOUNT	BALANCE
_____	_____	_____
_____	_____	_____
_____	_____	_____
_____	_____	_____

NOTES

_____

_____

_____

_____

_____

_____

_____

_____

_____

_____

_____

_____

MONTH OF: _____   WEEK OF: _____

DINNERS

_____

_____

_____

_____

_____

_____

_____

BREAKFASTS

_____

_____

_____

_____

_____

_____

_____

LUNCHES

_____

_____

_____

_____

_____

_____

SNACKS

_____

_____

_____

_____

_____

_____

SHOPPING LIST

PRICE	ITEM	STORE	NOTES

BUDGET FOR THE WEEK: _____

STORE	AMOUNT	BALANCE
_____	_____	_____
_____	_____	_____
_____	_____	_____
_____	_____	_____

NOTES

_____

_____

_____

_____

_____

_____

_____

_____

_____

_____

_____

_____

MONTH OF: _____   WEEK OF: _____

DINNERS	BREAKFASTS
_____	_____
_____	_____
_____	_____
_____	_____
_____	_____
_____	_____
_____	_____

LUNCHES	SNACKS
_____	_____
_____	_____
_____	_____
_____	_____
_____	_____
_____	_____

SHOPPING LIST

PRICE	ITEM	STORE	NOTES

BUDGET FOR THE WEEK: _____

STORE	AMOUNT	BALANCE
_____	_____	_____
_____	_____	_____
_____	_____	_____
_____	_____	_____

NOTES

_____

_____

_____

_____

_____

_____

_____

_____

_____

_____

_____

_____

_____

FREEZER INVENTORY

DATE ENTERED	ITEM	QTY	DATE EXPIRES	# USED

MONTH OF: _____   WEEK OF: _____

DINNERS	BREAKFASTS
_____	_____
_____	_____
_____	_____
_____	_____
_____	_____
_____	_____
_____	_____

LUNCHES	SNACKS
_____	_____
_____	_____
_____	_____
_____	_____
_____	_____
_____	_____

SHOPPING LIST

PRICE	ITEM	STORE	NOTES

BUDGET FOR THE WEEK: _____

STORE	AMOUNT	BALANCE
_____	_____	_____
_____	_____	_____
_____	_____	_____
_____	_____	_____

NOTES

_____

_____

_____

_____

_____

_____

_____

_____

_____

_____

_____

_____

MONTH OF: _____   WEEK OF: _____

DINNERS	BREAKFASTS
_____	_____
_____	_____
_____	_____
_____	_____
_____	_____
_____	_____
_____	_____

LUNCHES	SNACKS
_____	_____
_____	_____
_____	_____
_____	_____
_____	_____

SHOPPING LIST

PRICE	ITEM	STORE	NOTES

BUDGET FOR THE WEEK: _____

STORE	AMOUNT	BALANCE
_____	_____	_____
_____	_____	_____
_____	_____	_____
_____	_____	_____

NOTES

_____

_____

_____

_____

_____

_____

_____

_____

_____

_____

_____

_____

MONTH OF: _____ WEEK OF: _____

DINNERS	BREAKFASTS
_____	_____
_____	_____
_____	_____
_____	_____
_____	_____
_____	_____

LUNCHES	SNACKS
_____	_____
_____	_____
_____	_____
_____	_____
_____	_____

SHOPPING LIST

PRICE	ITEM	STORE	NOTES

BUDGET FOR THE WEEK: _____

STORE	AMOUNT	BALANCE
_____	_____	_____
_____	_____	_____
_____	_____	_____
_____	_____	_____

NOTES

_____

_____

_____

_____

_____

_____

_____

_____

_____

_____

_____

_____

MONTH OF: _____ WEEK OF: _____

DINNERS	BREAKFASTS
_____	_____
_____	_____
_____	_____
_____	_____
_____	_____
_____	_____
_____	_____

LUNCHES	SNACKS
_____	_____
_____	_____
_____	_____
_____	_____
_____	_____
_____	_____

SHOPPING LIST

PRICE	ITEM	STORE	NOTES

BUDGET FOR THE WEEK: _____

STORE	AMOUNT	BALANCE
_____	_____	_____
_____	_____	_____
_____	_____	_____
_____	_____	_____

NOTES

_____

_____

_____

_____

_____

_____

_____

_____

_____

_____

_____

_____

FREEZER INVENTORY

DATE ENTERED	ITEM	QTY	DATE EXPIRES	# USED

MONTH OF: _____ WEEK OF: _____

DINNERS

_____
_____
_____
_____
_____
_____

BREAKFASTS

_____
_____
_____
_____
_____
_____

LUNCHES

_____
_____
_____
_____
_____
_____

SNACKS

_____
_____
_____
_____
_____
_____

SHOPPING LIST

PRICE	ITEM	STORE	NOTES

BUDGET FOR THE WEEK: _____

STORE	AMOUNT	BALANCE
_____	_____	_____
_____	_____	_____
_____	_____	_____
_____	_____	_____

NOTES

_____

_____

_____

_____

_____

_____

_____

_____

_____

_____

_____

_____

_____

MONTH OF: _____   WEEK OF: _____

DINNERS

_____

_____

_____

_____

_____

_____

_____

BREAKFASTS

_____

_____

_____

_____

_____

_____

_____

LUNCHES

_____

_____

_____

_____

_____

_____

SNACKS

_____

_____

_____

_____

_____

_____

SHOPPING LIST

PRICE	ITEM	STORE	NOTES

BUDGET FOR THE WEEK: _____

STORE	AMOUNT	BALANCE
_____	_____	_____
_____	_____	_____
_____	_____	_____
_____	_____	_____

NOTES

_____

_____

_____

_____

_____

_____

_____

_____

_____

_____

_____

_____

MONTH OF: _____   WEEK OF: _____

DINNERS

_____

_____

_____

_____

_____

_____

_____

BREAKFASTS

_____

_____

_____

_____

_____

_____

_____

LUNCHES

_____

_____

_____

_____

_____

SNACKS

_____

_____

_____

_____

_____

SHOPPING LIST

PRICE	ITEM	STORE	NOTES

BUDGET FOR THE WEEK: _____

STORE	AMOUNT	BALANCE
_____	_____	_____
_____	_____	_____
_____	_____	_____
_____	_____	_____

NOTES

_____

_____

_____

_____

_____

_____

_____

_____

_____

_____

_____

_____

MONTH OF: _____   WEEK OF: _____

DINNERS	BREAKFASTS
_____	_____
_____	_____
_____	_____
_____	_____
_____	_____
_____	_____

LUNCHES	SNACKS
_____	_____
_____	_____
_____	_____
_____	_____
_____	_____

SHOPPING LIST

PRICE	ITEM	STORE	NOTES

BUDGET FOR THE WEEK: _____

STORE	AMOUNT	BALANCE
_____	_____	_____
_____	_____	_____
_____	_____	_____
_____	_____	_____

NOTES

_____

_____

_____

_____

_____

_____

_____

_____

_____

_____

_____

_____

_____

FREEZER INVENTORY

DATE ENTERED	ITEM	QTY	DATE EXPIRES	# USED

MONTH OF: _____   WEEK OF: _____

DINNERS	BREAKFASTS

LUNCHES	SNACKS

SHOPPING LIST

PRICE	ITEM	STORE	NOTES

BUDGET FOR THE WEEK: _____

STORE	AMOUNT	BALANCE
_____	_____	_____
_____	_____	_____
_____	_____	_____
_____	_____	_____

NOTES

_____

_____

_____

_____

_____

_____

_____

_____

_____

_____

_____

_____

_____

MONTH OF: _____   WEEK OF: _____

DINNERS	BREAKFASTS
_____	_____

DINNERS

_____

_____

_____

_____

_____

_____

BREAKFASTS

_____

_____

_____

_____

_____

_____

LUNCHES

_____

_____

_____

_____

_____

_____

SNACKS

_____

_____

_____

_____

_____

_____

SHOPPING LIST

PRICE	ITEM	STORE	NOTES
————	————————	————	————
————	————————	————	————
————	————————	————	————
————	————————	————	————
————	————————	————	————
————	————————	————	————
————	————————	————	————
————	————————	————	————
————	————————	————	————
————	————————	————	————
————	————————	————	————
————	————————	————	————
————	————————	————	————
————	————————	————	————
————	————————	————	————
————	————————	————	————
————	————————	————	————
————	————————	————	————

BUDGET FOR THE WEEK: _____

STORE	AMOUNT	BALANCE
_____	_____	_____
_____	_____	_____
_____	_____	_____
_____	_____	_____

NOTES

_____

_____

_____

_____

_____

_____

_____

_____

_____

_____

_____

_____

MONTH OF: _____   WEEK OF: _____

DINNERS

_____

_____

_____

_____

_____

_____

BREAKFASTS

_____

_____

_____

_____

_____

_____

LUNCHES

_____

_____

_____

_____

_____

_____

SNACKS

_____

_____

_____

_____

_____

_____

SHOPPING LIST

PRICE	ITEM	STORE	NOTES

BUDGET FOR THE WEEK: _____

STORE	AMOUNT	BALANCE
_____	_____	_____
_____	_____	_____
_____	_____	_____
_____	_____	_____

NOTES

_____

_____

_____

_____

_____

_____

_____

_____

_____

_____

_____

_____

_____

MONTH OF: _____ WEEK OF: _____

DINNERS	BREAKFASTS
_____	_____
_____	_____
_____	_____
_____	_____
_____	_____
_____	_____
_____	_____

LUNCHES	SNACKS
_____	_____
_____	_____
_____	_____
_____	_____
_____	_____

SHOPPING LIST

PRICE	ITEM	STORE	NOTES

BUDGET FOR THE WEEK: _____

STORE	AMOUNT	BALANCE
_____	_____	_____
_____	_____	_____
_____	_____	_____
_____	_____	_____

NOTES

_____

_____

_____

_____

_____

_____

_____

_____

_____

_____

_____

_____

FREEZER INVENTORY

DATE ENTERED	ITEM	QTY	DATE EXPIRES	# USED

MONTH OF: _____ WEEK OF: _____

DINNERS	BREAKFASTS
_____	_____
_____	_____
_____	_____
_____	_____
_____	_____
_____	_____

LUNCHES	SNACKS
_____	_____
_____	_____
_____	_____
_____	_____
_____	_____

SHOPPING LIST

PRICE	ITEM	STORE	NOTES

BUDGET FOR THE WEEK: _____

STORE	AMOUNT	BALANCE
_____	_____	_____
_____	_____	_____
_____	_____	_____
_____	_____	_____

NOTES

_____

_____

_____

_____

_____

_____

_____

_____

_____

_____

_____

MONTH OF: _____   WEEK OF: _____

DINNERS	BREAKFASTS

LUNCHES	SNACKS

SHOPPING LIST

PRICE	ITEM	STORE	NOTES

BUDGET FOR THE WEEK: _____

STORE	AMOUNT	BALANCE
_____	_____	_____
_____	_____	_____
_____	_____	_____
_____	_____	_____

NOTES

_____

_____

_____

_____

_____

_____

_____

_____

_____

_____

_____

_____

_____

MONTH OF: _____ WEEK OF: _____

DINNERS	BREAKFASTS
_____	_____
_____	_____
_____	_____
_____	_____
_____	_____
_____	_____
_____	_____

LUNCHES	SNACKS
_____	_____
_____	_____
_____	_____
_____	_____
_____	_____
_____	_____

SHOPPING LIST

PRICE	ITEM	STORE	NOTES

BUDGET FOR THE WEEK: _____

STORE	AMOUNT	BALANCE
_____	_____	_____
_____	_____	_____
_____	_____	_____
_____	_____	_____

NOTES

_____

_____

_____

_____

_____

_____

_____

_____

_____

_____

_____

_____

MONTH OF: _____   WEEK OF: _____

DINNERS

_____

_____

_____

_____

_____

_____

BREAKFASTS

_____

_____

_____

_____

_____

_____

LUNCHES

_____

_____

_____

_____

_____

_____

SNACKS

_____

_____

_____

_____

_____

_____

SHOPPING LIST

PRICE	ITEM	STORE	NOTES

BUDGET FOR THE WEEK: _____

STORE	AMOUNT	BALANCE
_____	_____	_____
_____	_____	_____
_____	_____	_____
_____	_____	_____

NOTES

_____

_____

_____

_____

_____

_____

_____

_____

_____

_____

_____

_____

_____

FREEZER INVENTORY

DATE ENTERED	ITEM	QTY	DATE EXPIRES	# USED

MONTH OF: _____   WEEK OF: _____

DINNERS

_____

_____

_____

_____

_____

_____

_____

BREAKFASTS

_____

_____

_____

_____

_____

_____

_____

LUNCHES

_____

_____

_____

_____

_____

_____

_____

SNACKS

_____

_____

_____

_____

_____

_____

_____

SHOPPING LIST

PRICE	ITEM	STORE	NOTES

BUDGET FOR THE WEEK: _____

STORE	AMOUNT	BALANCE
_____	_____	_____
_____	_____	_____
_____	_____	_____
_____	_____	_____

NOTES

_____

_____

_____

_____

_____

_____

_____

_____

_____

_____

_____

_____

MONTH OF: _____ WEEK OF: _____

DINNERS

_____

_____

_____

_____

_____

_____

BREAKFASTS

_____

_____

_____

_____

_____

_____

LUNCHES

_____

_____

_____

_____

_____

SNACKS

_____

_____

_____

_____

_____

SHOPPING LIST

PRICE	ITEM	STORE	NOTES

BUDGET FOR THE WEEK: _____

STORE	AMOUNT	BALANCE
_____	_____	_____
_____	_____	_____
_____	_____	_____
_____	_____	_____

NOTES

_____

_____

_____

_____

_____

_____

_____

_____

_____

_____

_____

_____

MONTH OF: _____ WEEK OF: _____

DINNERS	BREAKFASTS
_____	_____
_____	_____
_____	_____
_____	_____
_____	_____
_____	_____
_____	_____

LUNCHES	SNACKS
_____	_____
_____	_____
_____	_____
_____	_____
_____	_____
_____	_____

SHOPPING LIST

PRICE	ITEM	STORE	NOTES

BUDGET FOR THE WEEK: _____

STORE	AMOUNT	BALANCE
_____	_____	_____
_____	_____	_____
_____	_____	_____
_____	_____	_____

NOTES

_____

_____

_____

_____

_____

_____

_____

_____

_____

_____

_____

_____

_____

MONTH OF: _____ WEEK OF: _____

DINNERS	BREAKFASTS
_____	_____
_____	_____
_____	_____
_____	_____
_____	_____
_____	_____

LUNCHES	SNACKS
_____	_____
_____	_____
_____	_____
_____	_____
_____	_____
_____	_____

SHOPPING LIST

PRICE	ITEM	STORE	NOTES

BUDGET FOR THE WEEK: _____

STORE	AMOUNT	BALANCE
_____	_____	_____
_____	_____	_____
_____	_____	_____
_____	_____	_____

NOTES

_____

_____

_____

_____

_____

_____

_____

_____

_____

_____

_____

_____

FREEZER INVENTORY

DATE ENTERED	ITEM	QTY	DATE EXPIRES	# USED

MONTH OF: _____   WEEK OF: _____

DINNERS	BREAKFASTS
_____	_____
_____	_____
_____	_____
_____	_____
_____	_____
_____	_____

LUNCHES	SNACKS
_____	_____
_____	_____
_____	_____
_____	_____
_____	_____

SHOPPING LIST

PRICE	ITEM	STORE	NOTES

BUDGET FOR THE WEEK: _____

STORE	AMOUNT	BALANCE
_____	_____	_____
_____	_____	_____
_____	_____	_____
_____	_____	_____

NOTES

_____

_____

_____

_____

_____

_____

_____

_____

_____

_____

_____

_____

_____

MONTH OF: _____   WEEK OF: _____

DINNERS	BREAKFASTS
_____	_____
_____	_____
_____	_____
_____	_____
_____	_____
_____	_____

LUNCHES	SNACKS
_____	_____
_____	_____
_____	_____
_____	_____
_____	_____
_____	_____

SHOPPING LIST

PRICE	ITEM	STORE	NOTES

BUDGET FOR THE WEEK: _____

STORE	AMOUNT	BALANCE
_____	_____	_____
_____	_____	_____
_____	_____	_____
_____	_____	_____

NOTES

_____

_____

_____

_____

_____

_____

_____

_____

_____

_____

_____

_____

_____

_____

MONTH OF: _____ WEEK OF: _____

DINNERS	BREAKFASTS
_____	_____
_____	_____
_____	_____
_____	_____
_____	_____
_____	_____

LUNCHES	SNACKS
_____	_____
_____	_____
_____	_____
_____	_____
_____	_____

SHOPPING LIST

PRICE	ITEM	STORE	NOTES

BUDGET FOR THE WEEK: _____

STORE	AMOUNT	BALANCE
_____	_____	_____
_____	_____	_____
_____	_____	_____
_____	_____	_____

NOTES

_____

_____

_____

_____

_____

_____

_____

_____

_____

_____

_____

_____

MONTH OF: _____   WEEK OF: _____

DINNERS	BREAKFASTS
_____	_____
_____	_____
_____	_____
_____	_____
_____	_____
_____	_____
_____	_____

LUNCHES	SNACKS
_____	_____
_____	_____
_____	_____
_____	_____
_____	_____

SHOPPING LIST

PRICE	ITEM	STORE	NOTES

BUDGET FOR THE WEEK: _____

STORE	AMOUNT	BALANCE
_____	_____	_____
_____	_____	_____
_____	_____	_____
_____	_____	_____

NOTES

_____

_____

_____

_____

_____

_____

_____

_____

_____

_____

_____

_____

FREEZER INVENTORY

DATE ENTERED	ITEM	QTY	DATE EXPIRES	# USED

MONTH OF: _____   WEEK OF: _____

DINNERS	BREAKFASTS
_____	_____
_____	_____
_____	_____
_____	_____
_____	_____
_____	_____

LUNCHES	SNACKS
_____	_____
_____	_____
_____	_____
_____	_____
_____	_____
_____	_____

SHOPPING LIST

PRICE	ITEM	STORE	NOTES

BUDGET FOR THE WEEK: _____

STORE	AMOUNT	BALANCE
_____	_____	_____
_____	_____	_____
_____	_____	_____
_____	_____	_____

NOTES

_____

_____

_____

_____

_____

_____

_____

_____

_____

_____

_____

_____

_____

MONTH OF: _____ WEEK OF: _____

DINNERS

_____
_____
_____
_____
_____
_____
_____

BREAKFASTS

_____
_____
_____
_____
_____
_____
_____

LUNCHES

_____
_____
_____
_____
_____

SNACKS

_____
_____
_____
_____
_____

SHOPPING LIST

PRICE	ITEM	STORE	NOTES

BUDGET FOR THE WEEK: _____

STORE	AMOUNT	BALANCE
_____	_____	_____
_____	_____	_____
_____	_____	_____
_____	_____	_____

NOTES

_____

_____

_____

_____

_____

_____

_____

_____

_____

_____

_____

_____

MONTH OF: _____ WEEK OF: _____

DINNERS	BREAKFASTS
_____	_____
_____	_____
_____	_____
_____	_____
_____	_____
_____	_____

LUNCHES	SNACKS
_____	_____
_____	_____
_____	_____
_____	_____
_____	_____

SHOPPING LIST

PRICE	ITEM	STORE	NOTES

BUDGET FOR THE WEEK: _____

STORE	AMOUNT	BALANCE
_____	_____	_____
_____	_____	_____
_____	_____	_____
_____	_____	_____

NOTES

_____

_____

_____

_____

_____

_____

_____

_____

_____

_____

_____

_____

_____

FREEZER INVENTORY

DATE ENTERED	ITEM	QTY	DATE EXPIRES	# USED

SPECIAL EVENT MEAL PLANNER PAGE 1

EVENT NAME: _____   DATE: _____

APPETIZERS	ENTREES	SIDE DISHES
_____	_____	_____
_____	_____	_____
_____	_____	_____
_____	_____	_____
_____	_____	_____
_____	_____	_____

DRESSING & SAUCES	DESSERTS	DRINKS
_____	_____	_____
_____	_____	_____
_____	_____	_____
_____	_____	_____
_____	_____	_____

SPECIAL EVENT TO-DO LIST PAGE 2

MAKE AHEAD	DAY BEFORE	NIGHT BEFORE
_____	_____	_____
_____	_____	_____
_____	_____	_____
_____	_____	_____
_____	_____	_____
_____	_____	_____
_____	_____	_____
_____	_____	_____
_____	_____	_____
_____	_____	_____
_____	_____	_____
_____	_____	_____
_____	_____	_____
_____	_____	_____
_____	_____	_____
_____	_____	_____
_____	_____	_____

SPECIAL EVENT DAY OF LIST PAGE 3

TIME	TASKS	NOTES

SPECIAL EVENT MEAL PLANNER PAGE 1

EVENT NAME: _____   DATE: _____

APPETIZERS	ENTREES	SIDE DISHES
_____	_____	_____
_____	_____	_____
_____	_____	_____
_____	_____	_____
_____	_____	_____
_____	_____	_____

DRESSING & SAUCES	DESSERTS	DRINKS
_____	_____	_____
_____	_____	_____
_____	_____	_____
_____	_____	_____
_____	_____	_____

SPECIAL EVENT TO-DO LIST PAGE 2

MAKE AHEAD	DAY BEFORE	NIGHT BEFORE

SPECIAL EVENT DAY OF LIST PAGE 3

TIME	TASKS	NOTES

SPECIAL EVENT MEAL PLANNER PAGE 1

EVENT NAME: _____   DATE: _____

APPETIZERS	ENTREES	SIDE DISHES
_____	_____	_____
_____	_____	_____
_____	_____	_____
_____	_____	_____
_____	_____	_____
_____	_____	_____

DRESSING & SAUCES	DESSERTS	DRINKS
_____	_____	_____
_____	_____	_____
_____	_____	_____
_____	_____	_____
_____	_____	_____

SPECIAL EVENT TO-DO LIST PAGE 2

MAKE AHEAD	DAY BEFORE	NIGHT BEFORE

SPECIAL EVENT DAY OF LIST PAGE 3

TIME	TASKS	NOTES

SPECIAL EVENT MEAL PLANNER PAGE 1

EVENT NAME: _____   DATE: _____

APPETIZERS	ENTREES	SIDE DISHES
_____	_____	_____
_____	_____	_____
_____	_____	_____
_____	_____	_____
_____	_____	_____
_____	_____	_____

DRESSING & SAUCES	DESSERTS	DRINKS
_____	_____	_____
_____	_____	_____
_____	_____	_____
_____	_____	_____
_____	_____	_____
_____	_____	_____

SPECIAL EVENT TO-DO LIST PAGE 2

MAKE AHEAD	DAY BEFORE	NIGHT BEFORE
_____	_____	_____
_____	_____	_____
_____	_____	_____
_____	_____	_____
_____	_____	_____
_____	_____	_____
_____	_____	_____
_____	_____	_____
_____	_____	_____
_____	_____	_____
_____	_____	_____
_____	_____	_____
_____	_____	_____
_____	_____	_____
_____	_____	_____
_____	_____	_____
_____	_____	_____

SPECIAL EVENT DAY OF LIST PAGE 3

TIME	TASKS	NOTES

SPECIAL EVENT MEAL PLANNER PAGE 1

EVENT NAME: _____   DATE: _____

APPETIZERS	ENTREES	SIDE DISHES
_____	_____	_____
_____	_____	_____
_____	_____	_____
_____	_____	_____
_____	_____	_____
_____	_____	_____

DRESSING & SAUCES	DESSERTS	DRINKS
_____	_____	_____
_____	_____	_____
_____	_____	_____
_____	_____	_____
_____	_____	_____

SPECIAL EVENT TO-DO LIST PAGE 2

MAKE AHEAD	DAY BEFORE	NIGHT BEFORE

SPECIAL EVENT DAY OF LIST PAGE 3

TIME	TASKS	NOTES

SPECIAL EVENT MEAL PLANNER PAGE 1

EVENT NAME: _____   DATE: _____

APPETIZERS	ENTREES	SIDE DISHES
_____	_____	_____
_____	_____	_____
_____	_____	_____
_____	_____	_____
_____	_____	_____
_____	_____	_____

DRESSING & SAUCES	DESSERTS	DRINKS
_____	_____	_____
_____	_____	_____
_____	_____	_____
_____	_____	_____
_____	_____	_____
_____	_____	_____

SPECIAL EVENT TO-DO LIST PAGE 2

MAKE AHEAD	DAY BEFORE	NIGHT BEFORE
_____	_____	_____
_____	_____	_____
_____	_____	_____
_____	_____	_____
_____	_____	_____
_____	_____	_____
_____	_____	_____
_____	_____	_____
_____	_____	_____
_____	_____	_____
_____	_____	_____
_____	_____	_____
_____	_____	_____
_____	_____	_____
_____	_____	_____
_____	_____	_____
_____	_____	_____

SPECIAL EVENT DAY OF LIST PAGE 3

TIME	TASKS	NOTES

SPECIAL EVENT MEAL PLANNER PAGE 1

EVENT NAME: _____   DATE: _____

APPETIZERS	ENTREES	SIDE DISHES
_____	_____	_____
_____	_____	_____
_____	_____	_____
_____	_____	_____
_____	_____	_____
_____	_____	_____
_____	_____	_____

DRESSING & SAUCES	DESSERTS	DRINKS
_____	_____	_____
_____	_____	_____
_____	_____	_____
_____	_____	_____
_____	_____	_____
_____	_____	_____

SPECIAL EVENT TO-DO LIST PAGE 2

MAKE AHEAD	DAY BEFORE	NIGHT BEFORE

SPECIAL EVENT DAY OF LIST PAGE 3

TIME	TASKS	NOTES

CONVERSION CHART FOR FLOUR

METRIC	CUPS	OUNCE
15 GRAMS	2 TBSP	.563 OUNCE
32 GRAMS	¼ CUP	1.13 OUNCE
43 GRAMS	⅓ CUP	1.5 OUNCES
64 GRAMS	½ CUP	2.25 OUNCES
85 GRAMS	⅔ CUP	3 OUNCES
96 GRAMS	¾ CUP	3.38 OUNCES
128 GRAMS	1 CUP	4.5 OUNCES

CONVERSION CHART FOR LIQUIDS

METRIC	CUPS	FLUID OUNCE
15 ML	1 TBSP	½ FL. OZ
30 ML	2 TBSP	1 FL. OZ
60 ML	¼ CUP	2 FL. OZ
125 ML	½ CUP	4 FL. OZ
180 ML	¾ CUP	6 FL. OZ
250 ML	1 CUP	8 FL. OZ
500 ML	2 CUPS	16 FL. OZ
1,000 ML	4 CUPS	1 QUART

HOW TO ALTER A RECIPE

RECIPE USES	TO HALVE IT	TO DOUBLE IT
¾ CUP	6 TBSP	1 ½ CUPS
⅔ CUP	⅓ CUP	1 ⅓ CUPS
½ CUP	¼ CUP	1 CUP
⅓ CUP	2 TSP + 2 TBSP	⅔ CUP
¼ CUP	2 TBSP	½ CUP
1 TBSP	1 ½ TSP	2 TBSP
1 TSP	½ TSP	2 TSP
½ TSP	¼ TSP	1 TSP
¼ TSP	⅛ TSP	½ TSP

BAKING SUBSTITUTIONS

1 TSP BAKING POWDER	½ TSP CREAM OF TARTAR + ¼ TSP BAKING SODA
1 TSP BAKING SODA	3 TSP BAKING POWDER
1 CUP BUTTER	7/8 CUP COCONUT OIL OR 1 CUP PALM SHORTENING OR ½ CUP APPLESAUCE
1 CUP BUTTERMILK	1 TBSP LEMON JUICE + 1 CUP MILK
1 TBSP CORNSTARCH	1 TBSP ARROWROOT FLOUR OR CASSAVA FLOUR
1 TSP CREAM OF TARTAR	2 TSP VINEGAR OR 2 TSP LEMON JUICE
1 CUP SUGAR	1 CUP COCONUT SUGAR OR MAPLE SUGAR OR ¾ CUP HONEY OR MAPLE SYRUP
SOUR CREAM	PLAIN GREEK YOGURT
1 CUP CORN SYRUP	1 CUP HONEY
MAYONNAISE	GREEK YOGURT OR SOUR CREAM OR MASHED AVOCADO
HONEY	MOLASSES OR MAPLE SYRUP
BREAD CRUMBS	GROUND NUTS OR ALMOND FLOUR
1 TSP LEMON JUICE	1 TSP LIME JUICE OR ¼ TSP APPLE CIDER VINEGAR
FLOUR	CASSAVA FLOUR OR ALMOND FLOUR
1 EGG	1 TBSP CHIA SEEDS + 2 ½ TBSP WATER OR 1 TBSP FLAX SEEDS MIXED WITH 2 ½ TBSP WATER OR ½ A BANANA OR ¼ CUP CANNED PUMPKIN OR ¼ CUP CANNED SQUASH OR 2 TBSP POTATO STARCH

STAPLES LIST

EGGS	COCONUT OIL	PLASTIC WRAP
SALAD FIXINGS	NUT FLOUR	SARDINES
ONIONS	TOILET PAPER	WRAPS
MILK OF CHOICE	SEEDS	FOIL
FISH SAUCE	MAYONNAISE	NORI SHEETS
GELATIN	PAPER TOWELS	AVOCADOS
NUTS	SALT	PARCHMENT PAPER
COCONUT AMINOS	PALM SHORTENING	TEA
CHOCOLATE CHIP	FEMININE PRODUCTS	REUSABLE BAGS
SNACKS	CARROTS	COFFEE
DRINKS	COCONUT/MAPLE SUGAR	DISH SOAP
CACAO POWDER	TOOTHPASTE	HERBS
CRACKERS	JUICE	LAUNDRY SOAP
HUMMUS	FLOUR OF CHOICE	SUPPLEMENTS
FRESH FRUIT	SOAP	DISHWASHER SOAP
DRIED FRUIT	CANNED TUNA	MAPLE SYRUP
GUACAMOLE	NUT BUTTER	TOOTH BRUSHES
SPICES	SHAMPOO	RAW HONEY
AVOCADO OIL	CELERY	GARLIC
CUCUMBERS	BREAD	BEANS

STAPLES LIST CONTINUED

FAVORITE MEAL LIST

_____

_____

_____

_____

_____

_____

_____

_____

_____

_____

_____

_____

_____

_____

_____

_____

_____

_____

_____

_____

RECIPE: _____

INGREDIENTS:

_____   _____   _____   _____

_____   _____   _____   _____

_____   _____   _____   _____

DIRECTIONS:

_____   _____

_____   _____

_____   _____

_____   _____

_____   _____

RECIPE: _____

INGREDIENTS:

_____   _____   _____   _____

_____   _____   _____   _____

_____   _____   _____   _____

DIRECTIONS:

_____   _____

_____   _____

_____   _____

_____   _____

_____   _____

RECIPE: _____

INGREDIENTS:

_____ _____ _____ _____

_____ _____ _____ _____

_____ _____ _____ _____

DIRECTIONS:

_____ _____

_____ _____

_____ _____

_____ _____

_____ _____

RECIPE: _____

INGREDIENTS:

_____ _____ _____ _____

_____ _____ _____ _____

_____ _____ _____ _____

DIRECTIONS:

_____ _____

_____ _____

_____ _____

_____ _____

RECITPE: _____

INGREDIENTS:

_____ _____ _____ _____

_____ _____ _____ _____

_____ _____ _____ _____

DIRECTIONS:

_____ _____

_____ _____

_____ _____

_____ _____

_____ _____

RECIPE: _____

INGREDIENTS:

_____ _____ _____ _____

_____ _____ _____ _____

_____ _____ _____ _____

DIRECTIONS:

_____ _____

_____ _____

_____ _____

_____ _____

_____ _____

OTHER BOOKS BY ASHLEY AND MARCUS

1. Mama Bear Kusi's Blank Recipe Book: A Journal with Templates to Write and Organize All Your Favorite Recipes

2. Questions for Couples: 469 Thought-Provoking Conversation Starters for Connecting, Building Trust, and Rekindling Intimacy

3. Communication in Marriage: How to Communicate with Your Spouse Without Fighting

4. Emotional and Sexual Intimacy in Marriage: How to Connect or Reconnect with Your Spouse, Grow Together, and Strengthen Your Marriage

5. First Year of Marriage: The Newlywed's Guide to Building a Strong Foundation and Adjusting to Married Life.

6. My Tandem Nursing Journey: Breastfeeding Through Pregnancy, Labor, Nursing Aversion and Beyond.